THIS BOOK INCLUDES

- Over 30 Fun & Educational Projects

- 18 Math & Language Worksheets

- Art Projects with 40 Manipulatives

- Student Book Making Materials

- Bulletin Board Materials

- Learning Center Ideas and Materials

- Note Home to Parent and Unit Completion Certificate

FOODS and FOOD GROUPS

Welcome to Foods & Food Groups! This book provides you with materials to teach a fun and comprehensive unit on Food & Food Groups. All projects include blackline masters ready to go to work for you! We have included instructions for each project along with ideas you can use throughout your classroom. In addition, our patterns and blackline masters can be used in lots of ways to add fun and interest to this unit.

Our goal is to provide you with helpful and educational materials to make learning about Foods & Food Groups enjoyable for you and your students.

Bon Appetit!

Your partners in education,

KINGSLEY Publishing

ENGLISH and SPANISH in One Book

INSIDE THIS BOOK

Let's Eat Book
Munchy Mobile
Concentration
Flashcards
Food Groups Bingo
I Know My Food Colors Book
Food Groups Pyramid
Pizza Fractions

BLACKLINES
Language Development
Math Skills
Food Groups Recognition

Food Groups Puzzles
Take Home Note to Parents
Food Groups Completion Certificate
Bulletin Board Ideas

My Let's Eat Book

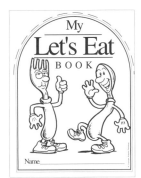

Students create and color their own "Let's Eat" book using food group manipulatives and write a new story!

ASSEMBLY INSTRUCTIONS

Copy 1 book for each student. Use construction paper for book cover & manipulatives. Use regular paper for inside book pages.

 Cut slots for manipulatives. OPTION: Students can glue manipulatives onto book page for one-time use.

Assemble and bind books using brads or staples.

 OPTION: Trim edges of pages as indicated by dotted lines.

Discuss balanced meals and healthy choices. Discuss and graph the times students eat their meals.

As a group make a class big book of the "Let's Eat" book, discussing meal times and healthy choices. Students make their own books in centers or as an independent project. Students choose food manipulatives to create their own balanced meal. Student shows the time they like to eat this meal on the clockface.

Students share their finished book with the class. Each author shares a story.

Munchy Mobile

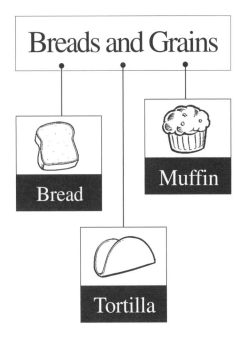

A fun art project! Use as classroom decorations throughout the unit.

Use mobiles to identify centers that focus on specific food groups.

ASSEMBLY INSTRUCTIONS

 Copy mobile "header" and corresponding food manipulatives.

 Have students decorate the food manipulatives. Use crayons, paint, markers, beans and glitter.

 Trim header and food manipulatives.

Use string, fishline, or dental floss to connect food manipulatives to header. Hang from the ceiling or walls.

Mi
Vamos a comer
LIBRO

Nombre: _____

Kingsley Publishing

My
Let's Eat
B O O K

Name:_____

Kingsley Publishing

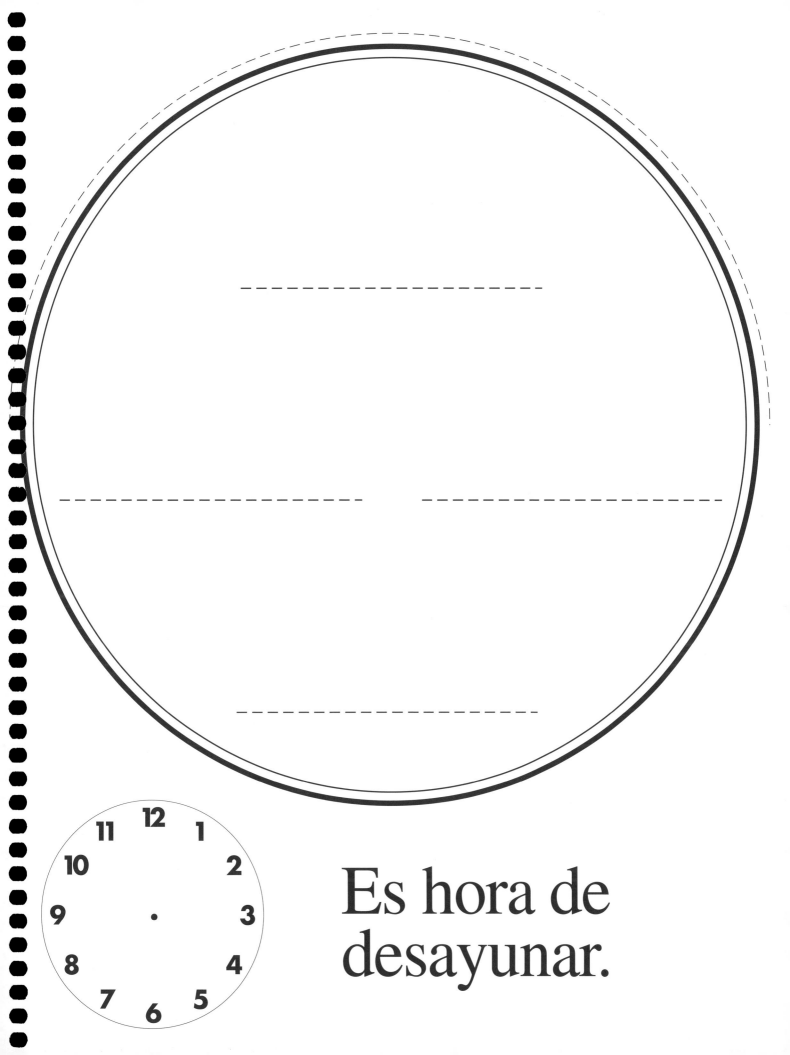

Es hora de
desayunar.

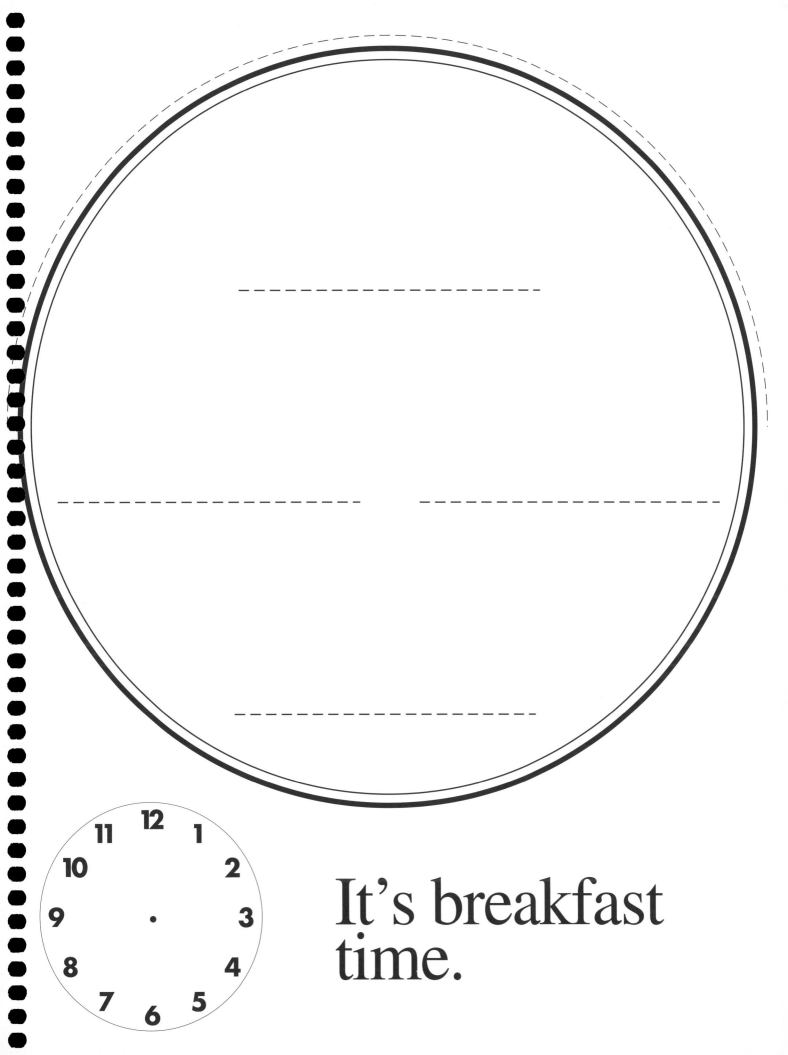

It's breakfast
time.

Mi cuento del desayuno

My Breakfast Story

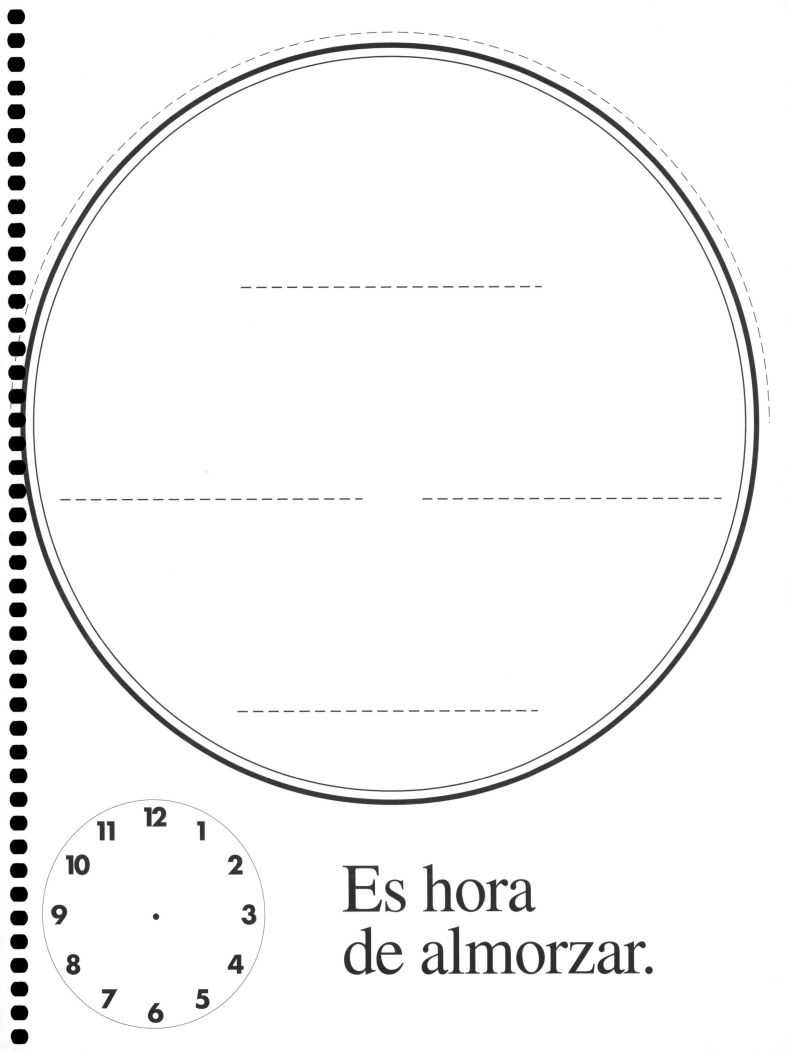

Es hora
de almorzar.

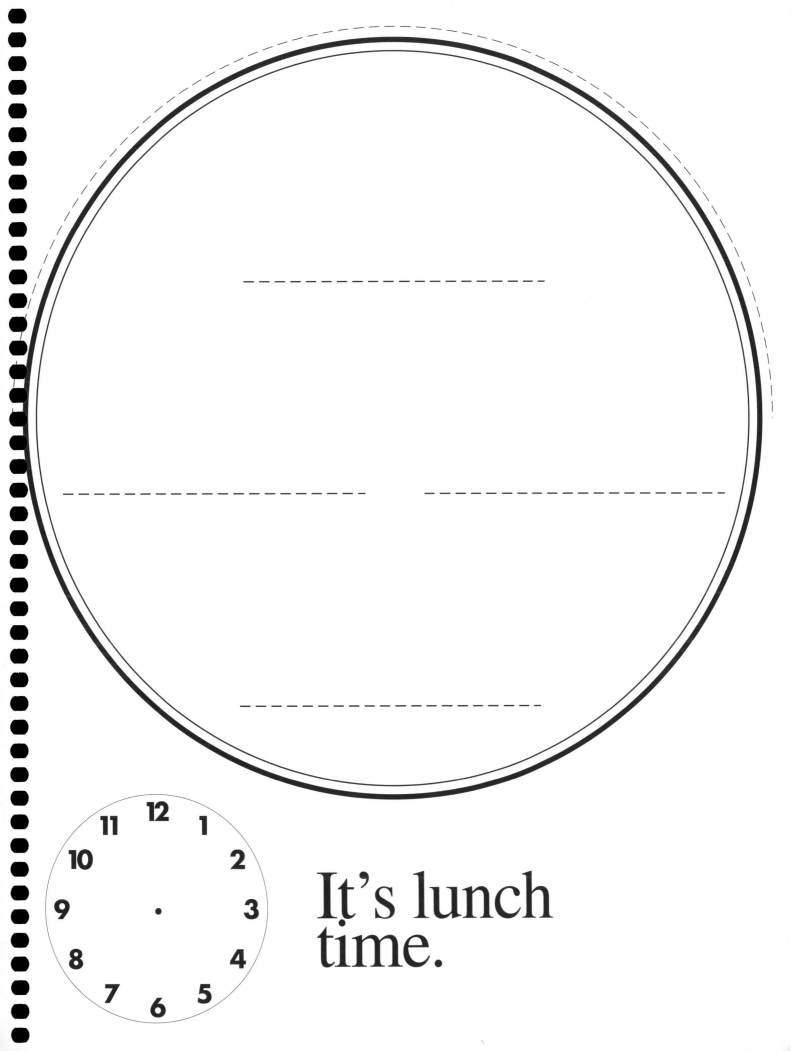

It's lunch
time.

Me gusta
el almuerzo

I Like
Lunch

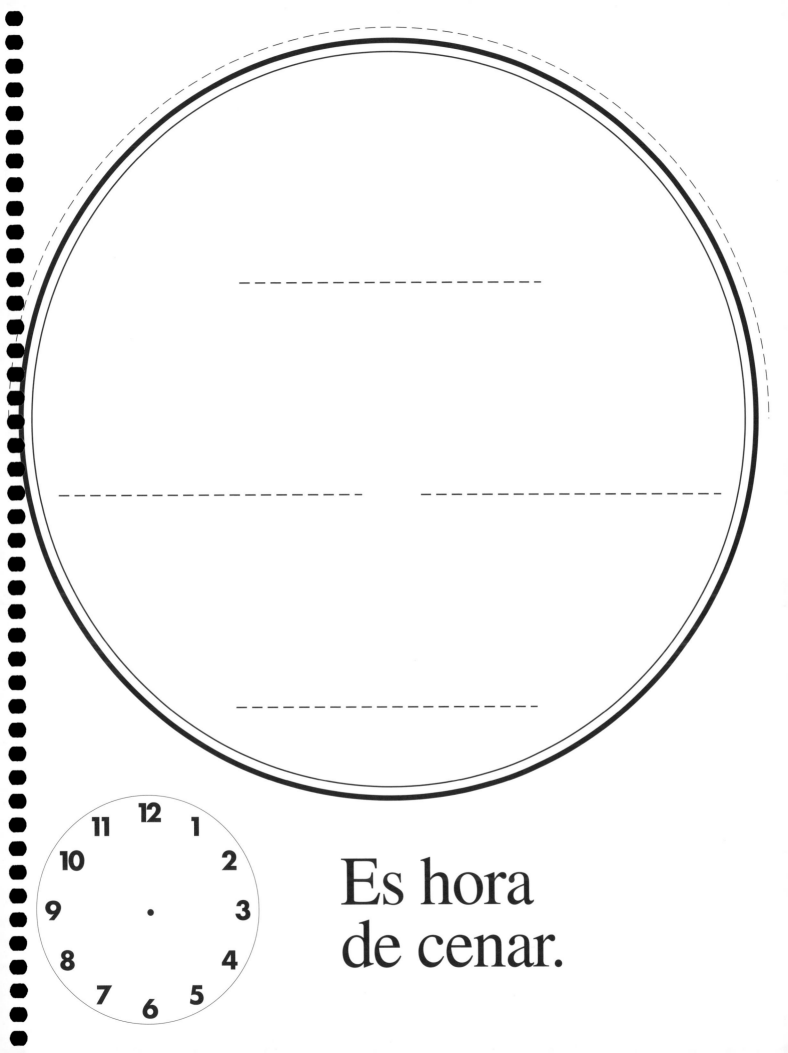

Es hora
de cenar.

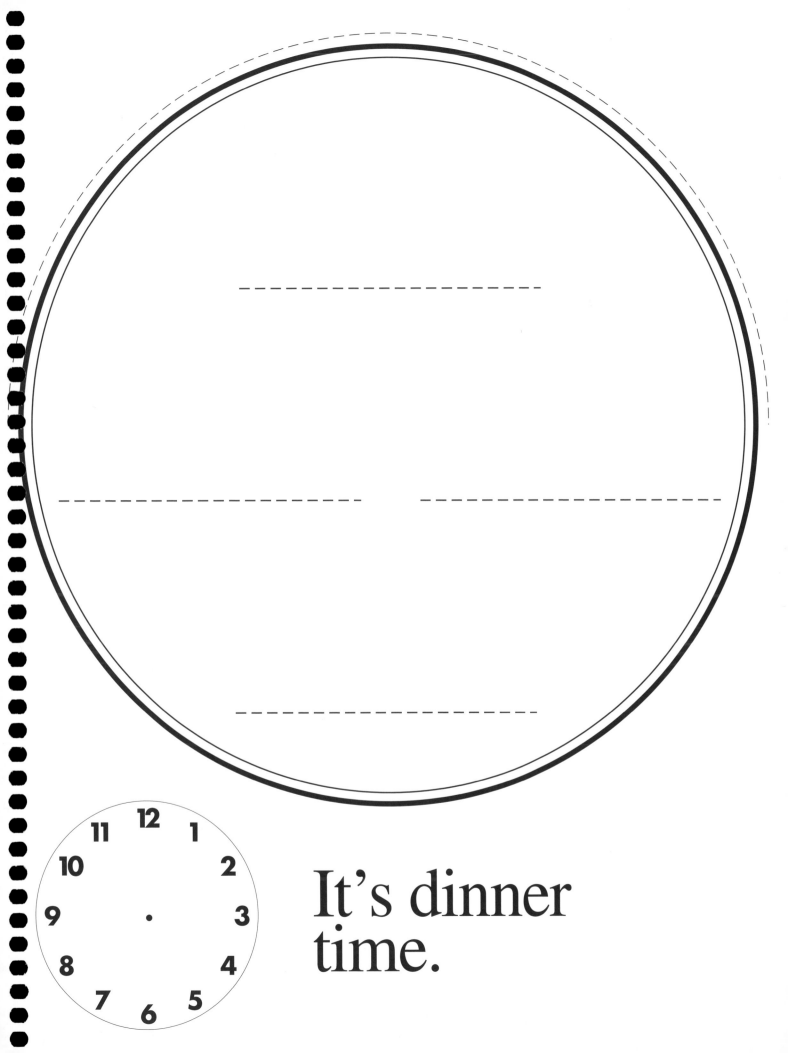

It's dinner
time.

Mi
cuento favorito
de la cena

My Favorite Dinner Story

Móvil de los alimentos

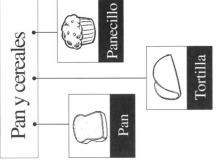

Pan y cereales

Panecillo

Tortilla

Pan

Kingsley Publishing

Carnes, frijoles y nueces

Alimentos extras

Pan y cereales

Frutas y vegetales

Leche y productos lácteos

Munchy Mobile

Kingsley Publishing

Breads and Grains

Muffin

Tortilla

Bread

Meats, Beans & Nuts

Extras–Oils and Sweets

Breads and Grains

Fruits / Vegetables

Dairy Products

Kingsley Publishing

Concentration

Using Food Group Manipulatives

This ever popular game helps children develop memory and matching skills. Best when played in small groups.

ASSEMBLY INSTRUCTIONS

 Copy 2 of each card onto construction paper or card stock.

 Cut manipulatives according to intended use.

CENTER IDEA To assist food group recogniton and/or to play as a specific food group center, copy each food group on different colored paper.

HOW TO PLAY

1. Mix up cards and lay them upside down in rows.

2. Students take turns choosing 2 cards at a time. If they choose 2 cards that are a match, they get another turn. If there is no match, the next player gets a turn. The player with the most matched pairs wins the game!

There are several variations of "Concentration" that you can try.

•**FOOD GROUP CONCENTRATION**-Use only cards from one food group. Separate your class into groups or use at centers, have one group play "Dairy Food Concentration," another "Bread & Grains Concentration."

• **WORD-PICTURE CONCENTRATION**-Cut out pictures and words separately. Lay out pictures and words (no need for 2 of each square). Have students play game by matching words to pictures as a "match."

• **WORD-WORD CONCENTRATION**-Cut out words only. Students match words with words. You may want to enlarge cards for this variation.

Flashcards

Using Food Group Manipulatives

The food manipulative pieces can be used in several ways as flashcards. We suggest you enlarge them if possible.

You may want to copy or glue manipulatives to cardstock for a longer lasting card. Laminate cards for permanent usage.

HOW TO PLAY

Use manipulatives as they appear in the book for remedial language cards. Have students verbalize picture and associate the written word on the card.

Cut words and pictures out separately, glue pieces back to back to create a traditional set of flashcards.

CENTER IDEA Use header cards from the "Munchy Mobile" and have children classify the cards according to the food group they belong to. Use pictures or word cards depending on student's level.

FLASHCARD VARIATIONS

Use manipulatives on an overhead projector for spelling exercises or food group lesson aids.

Show pictures and have students write the name of each one on the overhead as a language exercise.

Use manipulatives for math exercises:
"Count the dairy products"
"How many vegetables?"

Manipulantes de los Grupos

Pan y cereales

Frutas y vegetales

Leche y productos lácteos

Carnes, frijoles y nueces

Alimentos extras

Kingsley Publishing

pan

bagel

arroz

tortilla

panecillo	panqueque	cereal
pasta	uvas	zanahoria
manzana	naranja	tomate
papa	pera	lechuga

plátano	elote	chile
leche	helado	yogurt
queso	malteada	requesón
huevos	pollo	bistec

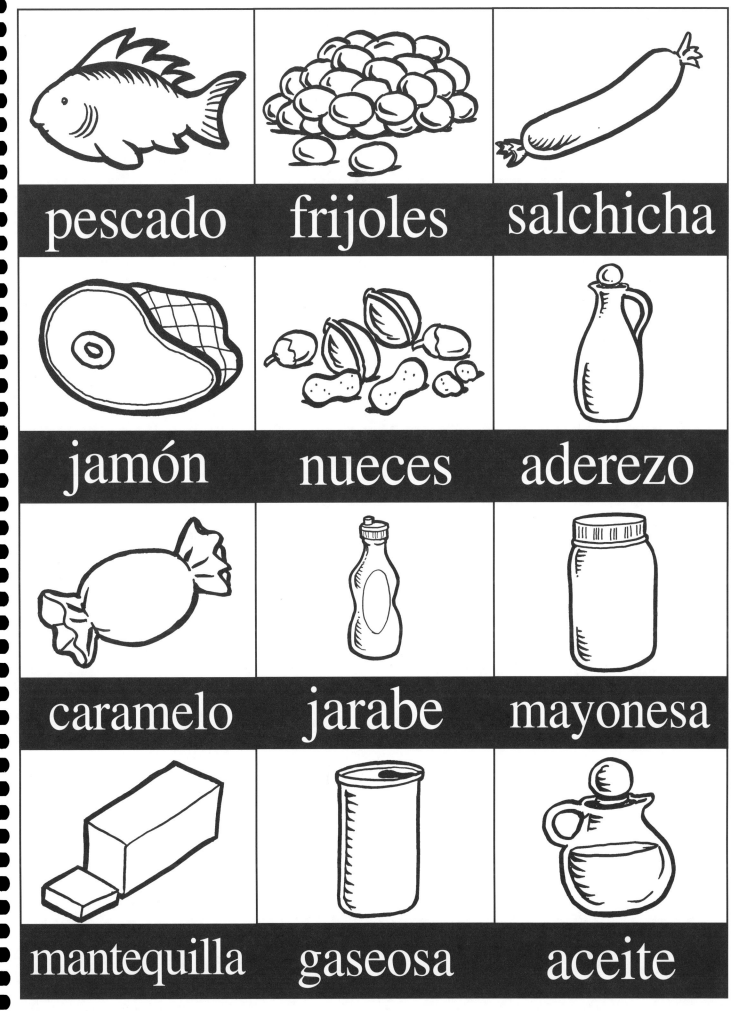

pescado	frijoles	salchicha
jamón	nueces	aderezo
caramelo	jarabe	mayonesa
mantequilla	gaseosa	aceite

Food Groups
Manipulatives

Breads and Grains
Fruits & Vegetables
Dairy Products
Meats, Beans & Nuts
Extras-Oil & Sweets

Kingsley Publishing

bread

bagel

rice

tortilla

muffin	pancake	cereal
pasta	grapes	carrot
apple	orange	tomato
potato	pear	lettuce

Kingsley Publishing

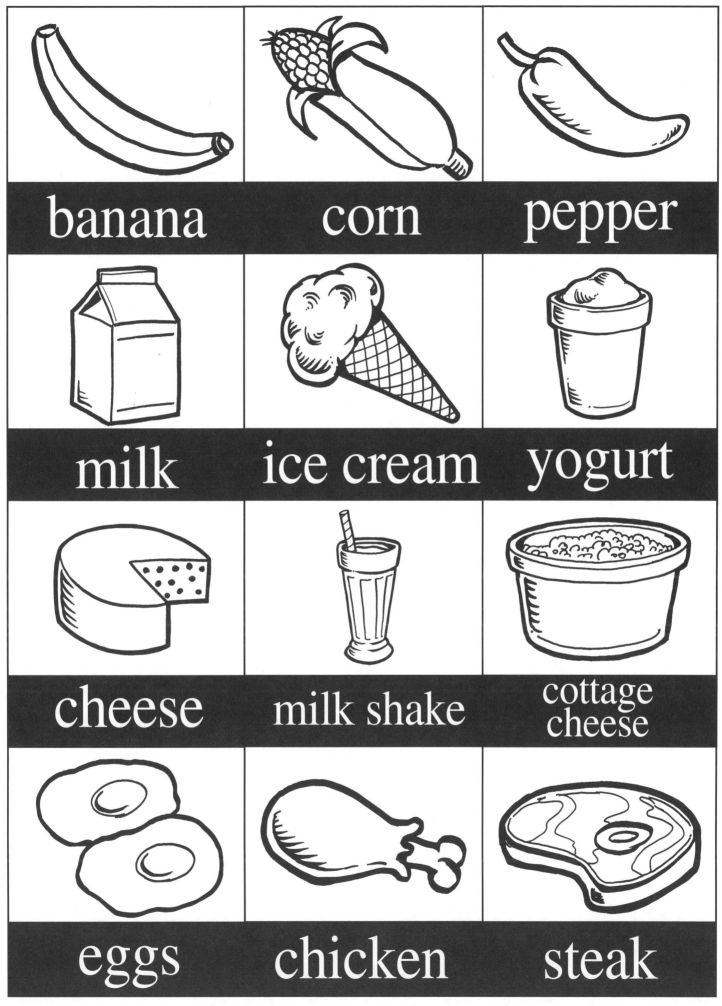

banana	corn	pepper
milk	ice cream	yogurt
cheese	milk shake	cottage cheese
eggs	chicken	steak

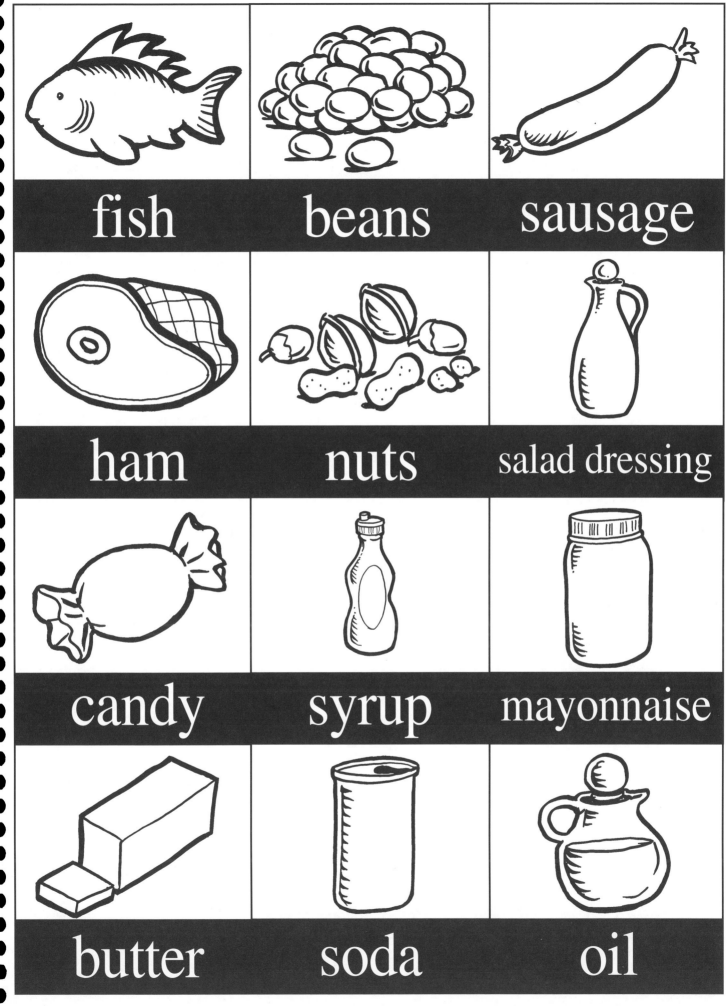

fish	beans	sausage
ham	nuts	salad dressing
candy	syrup	mayonnaise
butter	soda	oil

Food Group BINGO

Always a favorite, FOOD GROUP BINGO is designed to be played in groups of 5. There will be one winner from each group. Each group can be named a specific Food Group.

ASSEMBLY INSTRUCTIONS

 Copy bingo call words and the set of 5 bingo cards.

 Cut out call words if desired or randomly call words from list.

Use unifix cubes, beans, tiles or wooden blocks as black out squares.

HOW TO PLAY

Pick words or call out from list in random order. Students "mark-off" foods from their cards as they are called off.

OPTION

If desired, have the winner from each group play a "run off" game. The winners' "group" can receive a group prize, reward or privilege.

Food Group Puzzles

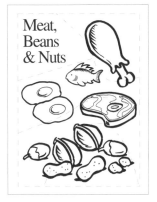

Students love to create and color their own puzzle.

ASSEMBLY INSTRUCTIONS

 Copy puzzles using card stock. Laminating puzzle pieces is suggested.

 Trim puzzles into pieces.

OPTION:
Color coding each puzzle helps students determine which pieces go to which puzzle. This is a great center activity!

Use completed puzzles on overhead or bulletin board

I Know My Food Colors Book

A great help for younger students to learn and reinforce their colors and color words.

ASSEMBLY INSTRUCTIONS

 Copy each page including cover and back page.

Fold pages in half and staple pages together on center line.

 Have students color each picture and write the correct color in each blank.

Vocabulario para el Bingo del grupo de alimentos

panecillo	pan	panqueque
pasta	arroz	bagel
cereal	tortilla	cereza
uvas	pera	manzana
chile	elote	zanahoria
plátano	papa	tomate
lechuga	naranja	leche
queso	helado	requesón
malteada	yogurt	salchicha
frijoles	jamón	huevos
pescado	pollo	bistec
nueces	aceite	jarabe
gaseosa	caramelo	mantequilla
mayonesa	aderezo	chocolate

Kingsley Publishing

Food Group Bingo Call Words

muffin	bread	pancake
pasta	rice	bagel
cereal	tortilla	cherry
grapes	pear	apple
pepper	corn	carrot
banana	potato	tomato
lettuce	orange	milk
cheese	ice cream	cottage cheese
milk shake	yogurt	sausage
beans	ham	eggs
fish	chicken	steak
nuts	oil	syrup
soda	candy	butter
mayonnaise	salad dressing	chocolate

Kingsley Publishing

Pan y cereales	Frutas y vegetales	Leche y productos lácteos	Carnes, frijoles y nueces	Alimentos extras
panecillo	zanahoria	malteada	pescado	jarabe
pan	naranja	helado	carne	dulce
panqueque	chile	GRATIS	frijoles	soda
bagel	pera	requesón	jamón	mantequilla
cereal	elote	leche	nueces	aderezo

Breads & Grains	Fruits/ Vegetables	Dairy Products	Meat,Beans & Nuts	Extras-Oils and Sweets
muffin	carrot	milk shake	fish	syrup
bread	orange	ice cream	steak	candy
pancake	pepper	FREE	beans	soda
bagel	pear	cottage cheese	ham	butter
cereal	corn	milk	nuts	salad dressing

Kingsley Publishing

Pan y cereales	Frutas y vegetales	Leche y productos lácteos	Carnes, frijoles y nueces	Alimentos extras
pan	pera	leche	pollo	jarabe
tortilla	plátano	queso	jamón	dulce
panqueque	naranja	GRATIS	huevos	soda
pasta	elote	yogurt	bistec	mantequilla
arroz	papa	helado	pescado	mayonesa

Kingsley Publishing

Breads & Grains	Fruits/ Vegetables	Dairy Products	Meat, Beans & Nuts	Extras-Oils and Sweets
bread	pear	milk	chicken	syrup
tortilla	banana	cheese	ham	candy
pancake	orange	FREE	eggs	soda
pasta	corn	yogurt	steak	butter
rice	potato	ice cream	fish	mayonnaise

Kingsley Publishing

Pan y cereales	Frutas y vegetales	Leche y productos lácteos	Carnes, frijoles y nueces	Alimentos extras
pan	papa	queso	pollo	aceite
bagel	plátano	leche	jamón	dulce
panqueque	naranja	GRATIS	salchicha	soda
cereal	elote	requesón	pescado	mantequilla
arroz	chile	malteada	carne	aderezo

Kingsley Publishing

Breads & Grains	Fruits/ Vegetables	Dairy Products	Meat, Beans & Nuts	Extras-Oils and Sweets
bread	potato	cheese	chicken	oil
bagel	banana	milk	ham	candy
pancake	orange	FREE	hot dog	soda
cereal	corn	cottage cheese	fish	butter
rice	pepper	milk shake	steak	salad dressing

Pan y cereales	Frutas y vegetales	Leche y productos lácteos	Carnes, frijoles y nueces	Alimentos extras
panecillo	uvas	queso	carne	mantequilla
tortilla	zanahoria	yogurt	frijoles	jarabe
pan	plátano	GRATIS	salchicha	dulce
arroz	tomate	requesón	pescado	aceite
cereal	pera	helado	huevos	soda

Kingsley Publishing

Breads & Grains	Fruits/ Vegetables	Dairy Products	Meat, Beans & Nuts	Extras-Oils and Sweets
muffin	grapes	cheese	steak	butter
tortilla	carrot	yogurt	beans	syrup
bread	banana	FREE	sausage	candy
rice	tomato	cottage cheese	fish	oil
cereal	pear	ice cream	eggs	soda

Kingsley Publishing

Pan y cereales	Frutas y vegetales	Leche y productos lácteos	Carnes, frijoles y nueces	Alimentos extras
arroz	lechuga	yogurt	frijoles	aderezo
cereal	manzana	leche	pescado	mantequilla
pasta	chile	GRATIS	jamón	jarabe
bagel	uvas	queso	huevos	dulces
pan	tomate	requesón	pollo	soda

Breads & Grains	Fruits/ Vegetables	Dairy Products	Meat,Beans & Nuts	Extras-Oils and Sweets
rice	lettuce	yogurt	beans	oil
cereal	apple	milk	fish	butter
pasta	pepper	FREE	ham	syrup
bagel	grapes	cheese	eggs	candy
bread	tomato	cottage cheese	chicken	soda

Frutas y vegetales

Fruits & Vegetables

Leche y productos lácteos

Dairy Products

Pan y cereales

Breads & Grains

Carnes, frijoles y nueces

Meats, Beans & Nuts

Yo sé mis colores de las comidas

Este libro fue creado por

Nombre: _____

Kingsley Publishing

I Know My Food Colors Book

This Book
Created By

Name: _____

Kingsley Publishing

El tomate es _____ .

El plátano es _____ .

Kingsley Publishing

The tomato is _____.

The banana is _____.

Kingsley Publishing

La lechuga es _____ .

La papa es _____ .

Kingsley Publishing

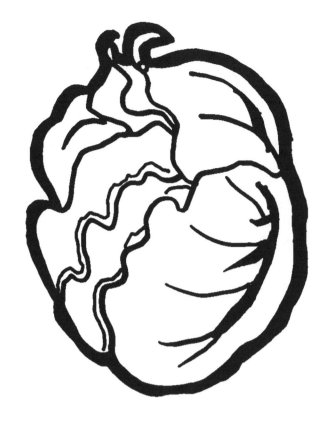

The lettuce is _____ .

The potato is _____ .

Kingsley Publishing

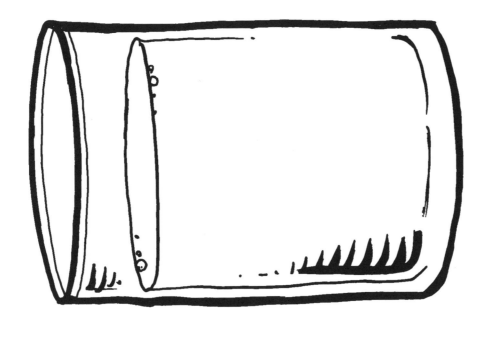

La leche es _____ .

La zanahoria es _____ .

Kingsley Publishing

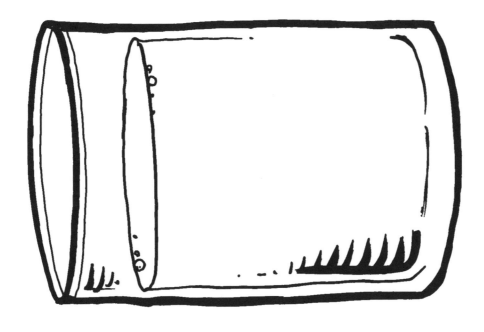

The milk is _____ .

The carrot is _____ .

Kingsley Publishing

Food Group Worksheets

We have included a variety of worksheets to support this unit.

The worksheets have been designed to cover three areas:
- LANGUAGE DEVELOPMENT–Language Arts
- MATH SKILLS
- FOOD GROUP RECOGNITION

MANY of the worksheets include 2 versions, to provide varied skill levels. Worksheets are labeled with the worksheet name and a "1" or "2" in the lower right corner. The "2" denotes a higher level difficulty.

LANGUAGE DEVELOPMENT WORKSHEETS
Food Names-1

Food Names-2

Word Match-1

Word Match-2

Fill In The Blanks-1

Fill In The Blanks-2

Fill In The Blanks-2

Word Find-1

Word Find-2

MATH SKILLS
Count The Foods

Food Math Problems-1

Food Math Problems-1

Food Story Problems-2

Food Story Problems-2

Word Count

Food Group Count

Pizza Fractions-Worksheet

FOOD GROUP RECOGNITION
Food Groups Worksheet

Nombre:_____

Nombres de los alimentos

Escribe el nombre de cada dibujo.

Name:_____

Food Names

Write the name of each food picture.

Nombre:_____

Nombres de los alimentos

Escribe el nombre de cada dibujo.

Name:_____

Food Names

Nombre:_____

Escoge la palabra

Haz una línea de la palabra al dibujo.

huevos

elote

pan

manzana

zanahoria

Name:_____

Word Match

Draw a line from the word to the matching picture.

eggs

corn

bread

apple

carrot

Nombre:_____

Escoge la palabra

Haz una línea de la palabra al dibujo.

pescado

panecillo

leche

queso

pollo

Name:_____

Word Match

Draw a line from the word to the matching picture.

fish

muffin

milk

cheese

chicken

Llena los espacios

 __eche

__aranja

 __uevos

__an

 __escado

__lote

Name:_____

Fill In the Blanks

Fill in the missing letter in each word.

mil__

orang__

__gg

brea__

__ish

cor__

Nombre:_____

Llena los espacios

 manzan__

ques__

 frijole__

lechug__

 uva__

tomat__

Name:_____

Fill In the Blanks

Fill in the missing letter in each word.

 a__ple

chee__e

 bea__s

lett__ce

 g__apes

to__ato

Nombre:_____

Llena los espacios

Me gusta comer tocino y _____.

A mi hermano le gusta el_____ para la cena.

Comimos sopa y _____ para el almuerzo.

Tomé jugo de _____ para el desayuno.

Preparamos un bocadillo de _____.

_____ son un bocadillo delicioso.

Hoy tomé _____ con cereal.

Comimos _____ para la cena.

Name:_____

Fill In the Blanks

Fill in the blanks in the sentences below. Use the food pictures as clues to the missing words.

I like to eat bacon and _____.

My brother likes _____ for dinner.

We had soup and _____ for lunch.

I drank _____ juice for breakfast.

We made a _____ sandwich.

_____ are a delicious snack.

I had _____ with cereal today.

We ate _____ for dinner.

Nombre:_____

Busca las palabras

¿Puedes encontrar las palabras escondidas?
Circulamos la palabra "pez" en este rompecabezas.
¿Puedes encontrar las otras palabras?

```
E S P A N D R S E L
K T O M A T E E N I
O D D F A R R O Z N
A T N S E T P E Z S
L T S M A N Z A N A
U T E T E D X G O T
V F E T L N R A E W
A I R R O N F H S R
S C T C T N E E A G
A R H A E L E C H E
```

pez   pan   elote   tomate
uvas   manzana   arroz   leche

Name:_____

Find the Words

Can you find the hidden words?
We circled "FISH" in this jumble.
Can you find the other words?

```
(f i s h) a c b p c o r n
 m i l k r t b e a n s k
 a p p l e h b r e a d p
 c r i c e x g r a p e s
 m u f f i n p m p i e z
 t o m a t o w p p e a r
 j e g g s a l s o d a r
```

(fish)   apple   rice   pear
grapes   corn   tomato   milk
bread   muffin   pie   beans

Can you find the bonus words?   __ggs   sod__

Nombre:_____

Busca las palabras

¿Puedes encontrar las palabras escondidas? Circulamos la palabra "desayuno" en este rompecabezas. ¿Puedes encontrar las otras palabras?

```
n  p  s  n  t  t  e  t  e  e  e  c
a  e  e  o  p  a  s  t  a  s  o  a
r  s (d  e  s  a  y  u  n  o) i  e
a  c  n  p  a  p  a  d  e  c  o  x
n  a  o  r  o  u  o  d  n  h  h  y
j  d  a  l  m  u  e  r  z  o  l  j
a  o  x  h  h  p  e  r  a  g  e  a
p  q  c  u  i  f  t  o  a  q  c  r
o  u  a  e  c  t  v  a  a  e  h  a
l  e  r  v  h  e  l  a  d  o  u  b
l  s  n  o  d  c  s  p  i  e  g  e
o  o  e  s  y  f  o  f  c  t  a  l
```

(desayuno)   huevos   pollo   jarabe

helado   almuerzo   queso   pera

naranja   pescado   carne   lechuga

             papa   pastas

Name: _____

Find the Words

Can you find the hidden words?
We circled "BREAD" in this jumble.
Circle the other words.

```
b a c o n q s t o m a t o
r w e r t y a u i u p l f
e g g a p p l e l f a e o
a s r n s d a g l f d t r
d h i g j l d r z i i t k
c i c e c r e a m n n u l
n a e y y u j p o b n c u
h a m b u r g e r c e e n
l v p i z z a s j d r t c
s p o o n s a n d w i c h
```

(bread)	sandwich	ice cream	bacon
tomato	lettuce	grapes	orange
rice	egg	hamburger	lunch
dinner	fork	oil	apple
salad	spoon	pizza	muffin

Nombre:_____

Cuenta los alimentos

Respuesta

_____

_____

_____

_____

_____

Name:_____

Count the Foods

How many of each
food can you count?

Answer

_____

_____

_____

_____

_____

Problemas de matemáticas

Escribe la respuesta de cada problema.

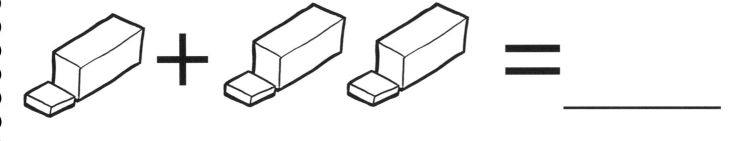 = _____

 = _____

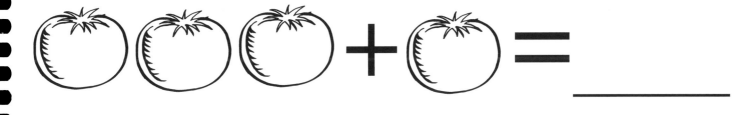 = _____

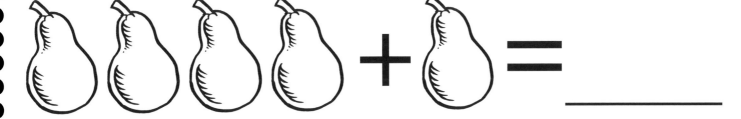 = _____

 = _____

Name:_____

Food Math Problems

Write the answer to each problem

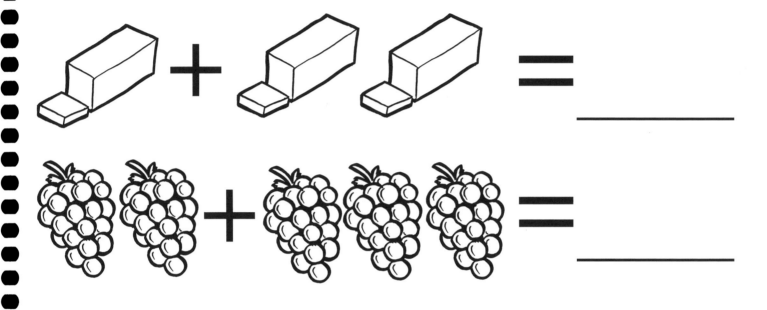

Nombre:_____

Problemas de matemáticas

Escribe la respuesta de cada problema.

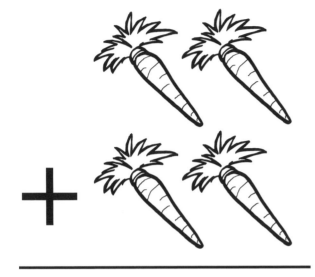

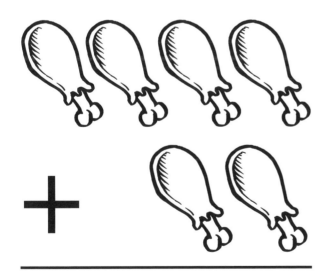

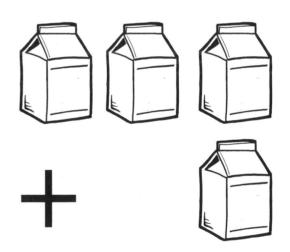

Name:_____

Food Math Problems

Write the answer to each problem.

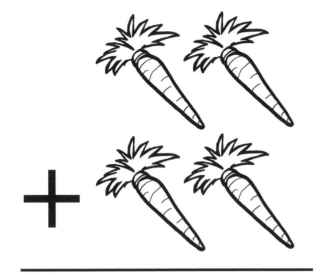

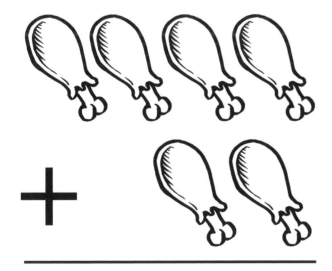

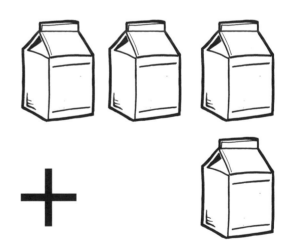

Nombre:_____

Cuentos de comida

Susana llenó su plato con zanahorias, pasta y un elote. Susana agregó un trozo de pollo a su plato. ¿Cuántos grupos de alimentos tiene Susana en su plato?_____.
Dibuja la comida en el plato de Susana.

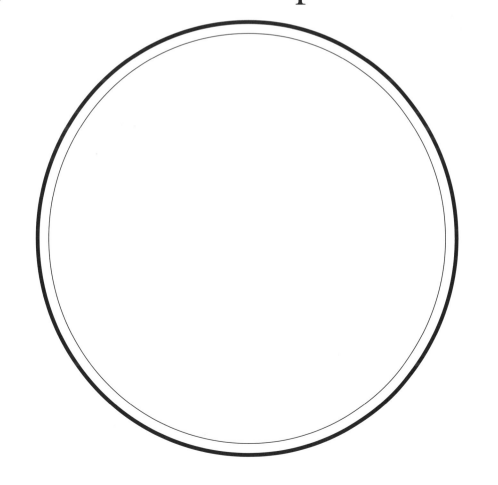

Name:_____

Food Story Problems

Sally filled her plate with carrots, pasta and corn. Sally added a piece of chicken to her plate. How many food groups does Sally have on her plate?_____.

Draw the food on Sally's plate.

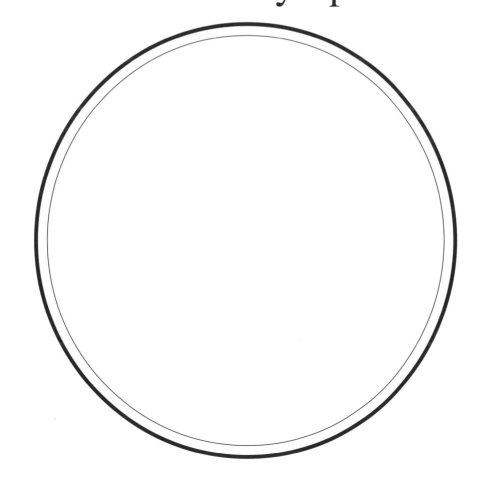

Nombre:_____

_____

Cuentos de comida

Tomás tenía una bolsa de 10 manzanas. Él le dio 2 a Marcos y 4 a José. ¿Cuántas manzanas tiene Tomás ahora? _____.

Pon una "X" en la tercera manzana a la izquierda. Colorea la primera manzana roja. Colorea la segunda manzana verde.

Linda tiene 4 manzanas. Ella escogió 5 más. Escribe la equación y la respuesta. Escribe tu propio problema.

Food Story Problems

Answer
each problem.

Tom had a bag of 10 apples. He gave 2 to
Tim and 4 to Jason. How many apples does
Tom have left? _____.

Put an "X" on the apple that is third from
the left. Color the first apple red. Color the
second apple green.

Linda has 4 apples. She picked 5 more.
Write the equation and answer.

Nombre:_____

Cuenta las palabras

Cuenta el número de alimentos en cada oración.

_____ Yo comí elote y frijoles hoy.

_____ Mi ensalada de fruta tenía una manzana, una pera y una naranja.

_____ Comimos pan y mantequilla en la cena.

_____ A mi hermana le gusta ensalada, pizza y gaseosa.

_____ Tomás tenía un panecillo, un plátano y dos huevos en su canasta.

_____ ¡Hoy mi hermano se comió tres plátanos con su leche y cereal!

_____ Mi bocadillo está hecho de dos trozos de pan, jamón, queso, lechuga y un pedazo de tomate.

_____ Yo comí pollo, arroz y un elote con un vaso de leche para la cena.

Word Count

Count the number of foods in each sentence.

_____ I ate corn and beans today.

_____ My fruit salad had an apple, a pear and an orange.

_____ We ate bread and butter with dinner.

_____ My sister likes salad, pizza and soda.

_____ Tom had a muffin, a banana and two eggs in his basket.

_____ My brother ate three bananas with his milk and cereal today!

_____ My sandwich is made of two pieces of bread, ham, cheese, lettuce and tomato.

_____ I had chicken, rice and corn for dinner with a glass of milk.

Nombre:_____

Grupos de alimentos

¿Cuántos alimentos puedes encontrar de cada grupo?

____ Leche y productos lácteos

____ Frutas y vegetales

____ Pan y cereales

____ Carnes, frijoles y nueces

____ Alimentos extras

Name:_____

Food Group Count

Count the foods from each food group. How many can you find from each food group?

_____ Dairy Products

_____ Fruits and Vegetables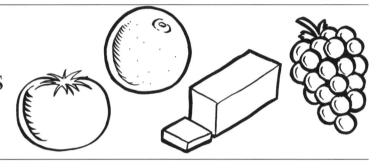

_____ Breads and Grains

_____ Meats, Beans and Nuts

_____ Extras-Oils and Sweets

Grupos de alimentos

Haz un círculo alrededor de los alimentos de cada grupo.

Pan y cereales

Frutas y vegetales

 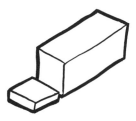  

Leche y productos lácteos

Carnes, frijoles y nueces

Alimentos extras

  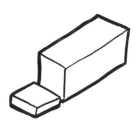 

Name:_____

Food Groups Worksheet

Circle the foods that belong to each food group.

Breads & Grains

Fruits & Vegetables

 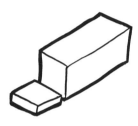  

Dairy Products

Meats, Beans & Nuts

Extras– Oils & Sweets

  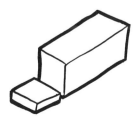 

Food Group Pyramid

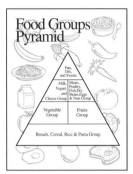

This page can be used in a number of different ways.

HOW TO USE
• Use it on an overhead projector or bulletin board as an aid during Food Group discussions.
• Cut out and laminate pieces for use as a puzzle.
• Copy and give one to each student as an individual study aid.
• Have each student color their own pyramid and use on classroom bulletin board.
• Have students take home their pyramid as a reminder to mom and dad of good nutrition guidelines.

Pizza Fractions

Center idea or whole class activity. Math fun with fractions!

ASSEMBLY INSTRUCTIONS

 Copy pizza plate & fractions. One per student.

 Cut out fractions.

 Students glue on fractions that will result in a whole pizza pie!

 Use in conjunction with the "Pizza Fractions" worksheet on a overhead projector or on a bulletin board.
Use fractions as individual student manipulatives during class discussions. Laminate and color code pieces for long lasting center aids.

EXTRA IDEAS
Use your students themselves to physically demonstrate "fractions" concepts. Separate students into groups of 1/3 and 2/3, 1/2 and 1/2, 3/4 and 1/4, etc.

Food Group Certificate

These are a great way to recognize and reward your students as they progress through the food group unit.

HOW TO USE

Use as a specific incentive when students finish a defined list of projects or as a general award when the unit is complete. These make a great classroom bulletin board theme and provides students a take home diploma they can be proud of.

Let students color their own certificate as a classroom art project or copy on colored paper.

Dear Parent Letter

Send this note home with students to let their parents know what is going on in their classroom. Provides an introduction to parents of the upcoming unit.

 Sign and copy.

Pirámide de los grupos de alimentos

Alimentos extras

Grupo de leche, yogurt y queso

Grupo de carne, pollo, pescado, frijoles, huevos y nueces

Grupo de vegetales

Grupo de frutas

Grupo de pan, cereales, arroz y pasta

Una dieta ideal incluye una variedad saludable de alimentos de cada uno de estos grupos básicos.

Los alimentos deben comerse en proporcíones ilustradas por esta pirámide.

Food Groups Pyramid

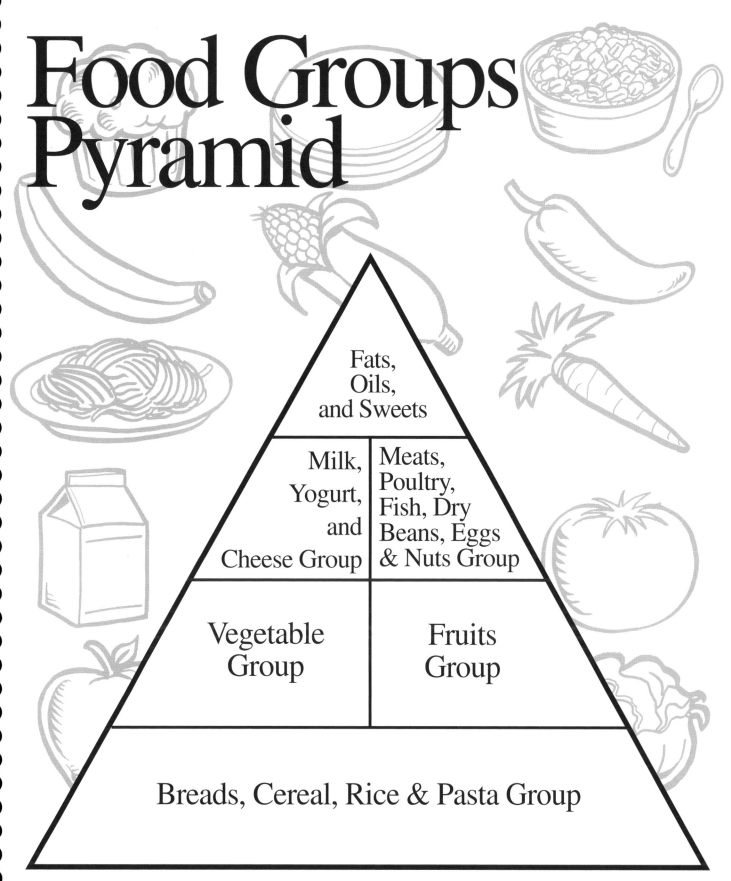

Fats,
Oils,
and Sweets

Milk,
Yogurt,
and
Cheese Group

Meats,
Poultry,
Fish, Dry
Beans, Eggs
& Nuts Group

Vegetable
Group

Fruits
Group

Breads, Cereal, Rice & Pasta Group

The ideal diet includes a healthy variety of foods from each of these basic food groups. Foods should be eaten in proportions illustrated by this pyramid.

Kingsley Publishing

Fracciones de pizza

¿Cuánta pizza hay en cada plato?

1   1/3

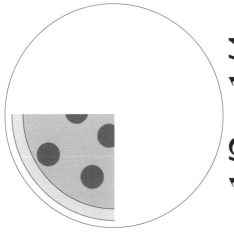

1/2   1/4

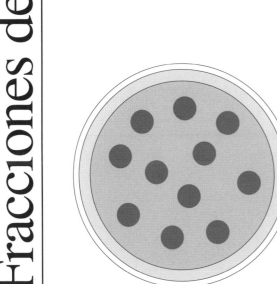

1/3   1/2

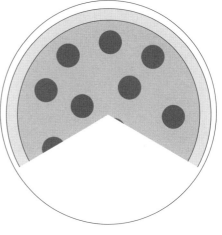

3/4   2/3

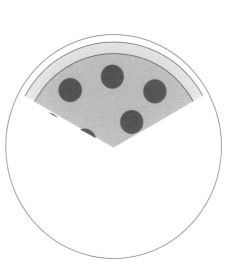

1/4   1/3

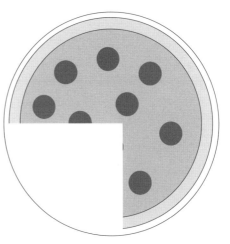

2/3   1/2

Kingsley Publishing

Pizza Fractions

Circle the correct fraction shown below each pizza picture.

How much pizza is on each plate?

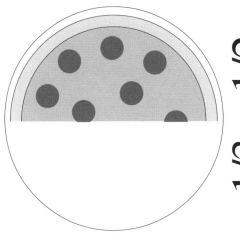

1   1/3

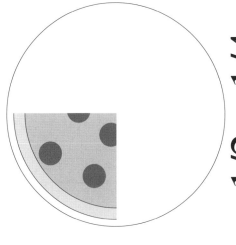

1/2   1/4

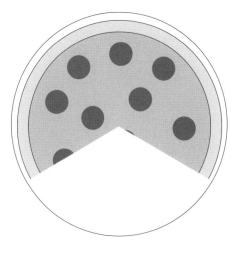

1/3   1/2

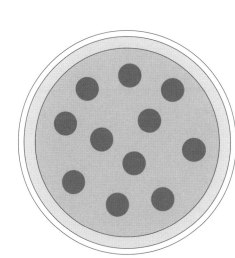

3/4   2/3

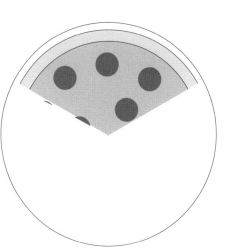

1/4   1/3

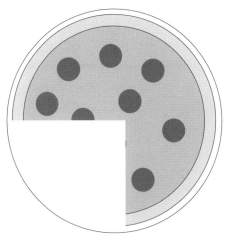

2/3   1/2

Fracciones de pizza

¡Es la hora de la pizza! ¿Puedes hacer toda una pizza usando los trozos de fracciones?

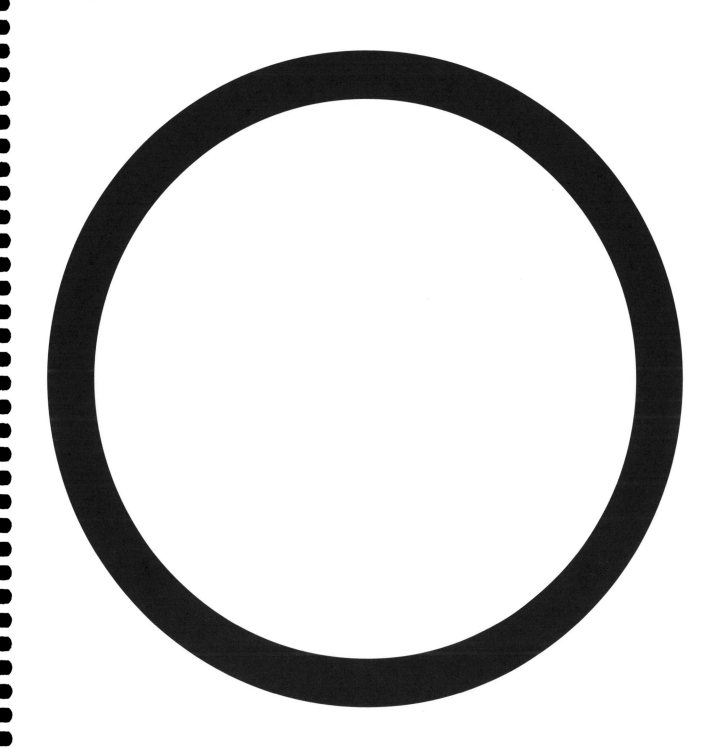

Kingsley Publishing

Pizza Fractions

It's pizza time! Can you make up a whole pizza using the fraction pieces?

Kingsley Publishing

Estimados Padres,

Comenzaremos a estudiar nuestra unidad de Las comidas y Grupos de alimentos. Aprenderemos sobre las comidas balanceadas y las comidas en cada grupo.

Por favor, platiquen durante la cena acera de los alimentos que están comiendo. Conversaciones de familia ayudan a los estudiantes a entender los conceptos de la clase!

Atentamente,

_____

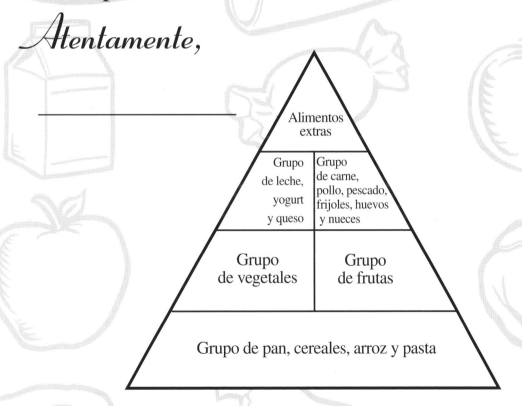

Alimentos extras

Grupo de leche, yogurt y queso

Grupo de carne, pollo, pescado, frijoles, huevos y nueces

Grupo de vegetales

Grupo de frutas

Grupo de pan, cereales, arroz y pasta

Pirámide de los grupos de alimentos

Una dieta ideal incluye una variedad saludable de alimentos de cada uno de estos grupos básicos.

Los alimentos deben comerse en proporcíones ilustradas por esta pirámide.

Kingsley Publishing

Dear Parent,

We are starting our unit on Foods & Food Groups. We will learn about balanced meals and the foods in each food group.

Please take a moment during your meals to discuss the foods you are eating. Family discussions will help reinforce concepts being learned in class!

Sincerely,

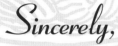

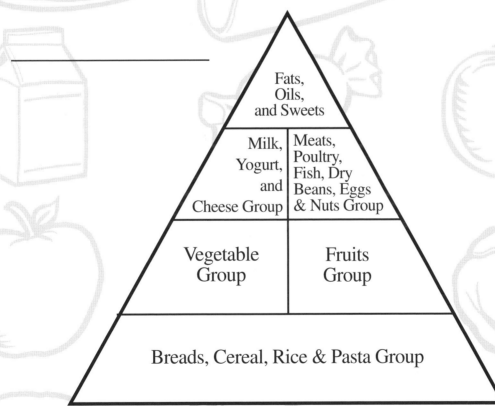

Fats,
Oils,
and Sweets

Milk, Yogurt, and Cheese Group | Meats, Poultry, Fish, Dry Beans, Eggs & Nuts Group

Vegetable Group | Fruits Group

Breads, Cereal, Rice & Pasta Group

The Food Groups Pyramid

The ideal diet includes a healthy variety of foods from each of these basic food groups. Foods should be eaten in proportions illustrated by this pyramid.

Kingsley Publishing

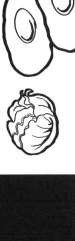

¡Yo sé de mis grupos de alimentos!

Alimentos y sus grupos

CERTIFICADO

Nombre: _____

Has comenzado una vida

saludable al haber aprendido

a comer buenos alimentos.

CERTIFICATE

FOODS
and FOOD GROUPS

I Know My
Food
Groups

Name:

You are on your way

to a healthier life

by learning good

eating habits.

Kingsley Publishing

Bulletin Board Ideas

• Copy any of the food group manipulative pictures onto overhead transparency paper to enlarge. Trace onto butcher paper. Use enlarged picture to decorate bulletin boards.

• Use blackline to make a transparency of the food groups pyramid and trace onto butcher paper. Have students cut out pictures of foods from a magazine and classify foods by gluing in the correct food group.

OPTION: Select one food group and follow above. – Use "Munchy Mobile" header cards.

• Again use your overhead to trace pictures of food from one or all food groups. Cut out 2 patterns for each food. Have students paint them. Using newspaper to stuff your food, stapling 2 sides together – hang on walls or from ceiling.

• Have students color and cut their favorite food from the foods shown in this unit. Use these "foods" as a border for your food bulletin board.

• Make a giant place setting for your food bulletin board. As the unit progresses, have students recreate the plate by designing their own balanced meal.

• Make your bulletin board a table top. Give each student a paper plate. After you discuss balanced meals, have each student color their idea of a balanced meal on their plate. Glue onto the "table." As the unit progresses, review the plates on the table and let the students redraw their meals as they learn more and more. Great informal ongoing assessment idea.

Kingsley Publishing
A Division of Carson-Dellosa Publishing
Order Form

FASTEST ORDERING
Fax your order 7 days a week
24 hours a day!
FAX TOLL FREE: 1-866-249-2304

Mail your order to:
Carson-Dellosa Publishing Co., Inc.
P.O. Box 35665, Greensboro, NC 27425-5665

Billing Information ☐ HOME ☐ SCHOOL

COMPANY/NAME SCHOOL	
ADDRESS	
CITY, STATE, ZIP	
TELEPHONE	FAX

Delivery Information

Same As Billing
☐ YES, Check Here

NAME ▶	
ADDRESS	
CITY, STATE, ZIP	
TELEPHONE	

SPECIAL INSTRUCTIONS:

ITEM #	TITLE/DESCRIPTION	UNIT PRICE	QUANTITY	TOTAL
OUR BEST VALUE - KINGSLEY PUBLISHING PACKAGE DEALS!				
K44000	Complete Classroom Package - 25 Books! (16 Thematic Units & 9 Time Savers)	349.99		
K44001	Thematic Package - 16 Books!	219.99		
K44002	Teacher's Time Saver Package - 9 Books!	119.99		
THEMATIC UNITS - ENGLISH AND SPANISH IN EACH BOOK				
K04000	El Dinero/MONEY-Bills, Coins & Change	14.99		
K04001	Los Alimentos/FOOD & Food Groups	14.99		
K04002	La Hora/TIME & Clocks	14.99		
K04003	La Comunidad/THE COMMUNITY	14.99		
K04004	Los Insectos/INSECTS	14.99		
K04005	Las Arañas/SPIDERS	14.99		
K04006	La Granja/THE FARM	14.99		
K04007	Plantas/PLANTS	14.99		
K04008	Animales/ANIMALS	14.99		
K04009	Planetas/PLANETS	14.99		
K04010	Máquinas Sencillas/SIMPLE MACHINES	14.99		
K04011	Vida Marina/SEA LIFE	14.99		
K04012	Dinosaurios/DINOSAURS	14.99		
K04013	Transportación/TRANSPORTATION	14.99		
K04014	El Tiempo/WEATHER	14.99		
K04015	El Ciclo del Agua/WATER CYCLES	14.99		
TEACHER'S TIME SAVERS - ENGLISH AND SPANISH IN EACH BOOK				
K04016	FLASHCARD Super Book	14.99		
K04017	50 Student Books	14.99		
K04018	50 Student Mobiles	14.99		
K04019	Alphabet Blackline Masters	14.99		
K04020	200 High Frequency Sight Words	14.99		
K04021	Spanish/English Vocabulary Development	14.99		
K04022	50 Learning Center Activities	14.99		
K04023	Story Starters & Stationery	14.99		
K04024	Holiday Activities-Art Projects, Stationery, Invitations, Greeting Cards & More	14.99		

PAYMENT METHOD ☐ CHECK ENCLOSED ☐ MasterCard ☐ VISA

CARD NUMBER: _____

NAME ON CARD: _____ EXP. DATE: _____

SIGNATURE: _____

*Add Shipping & Handling	
For delivery in CA, CT, FL, IL, MI, NC, NJ, OH, TX or UT, add applicable sales tax. Orders must be submitted on a purchase order with a valid signature to receive tax exempt status.	
Total	

ADD SHIPPING & HANDLING

Under $25.00	$4.95
$25.01-$40.00	$8.95
$40.01-$55.00	$10.95
$55.01-$100	$12.95
Over $100	10% of order amount
Minimum order is $10.00	

*SHIPPING & HANDLING
Applies only to orders shipped within the continental United States. Alaska, Hawaii, Puerto Rico, and international customers, please call for shipping rates.

Payable in U.S. dollars only.

Purchase Orders Accepted *Purchase Order with valid signature must be included with mailed order form.*

Kingsley Publishing
A Division of Carson-Dellosa Publishing
Order by phone, Monday-Friday, 8:00am-7:00pm EST
(Visa or MasterCard only) - Minimum order $10.00
Phone Toll Free 1-866-250-6886 or 336-808-3263